BRISTOW'S
GUIDE TO LIVING

THIS NEEDS
LOOKING INTO....

BRISTOW'S
GUIDE TO LIVING

FRANK DICKENS

M

MACMILLAN LONDON

Illustrations copyright © Express Newspapers Limited 1982

Text copyright © Frank Dickens

ISBN 0 333 34125 2

First published 1982 by
Macmillan London Limited
London and Basingstoke

Associated companies in Auckland, Dallas,
Delhi, Dublin, Hong Kong, Johannesburg,
Lagos, Manzini, Melbourne, Nairobi,
New York, Singapore, Tokyo, Washington
and Zaria

Printed and bound in Great Britain
at The Pitman Press, Bath

Contents

How to Succeed in Business

Ode to Overtime

Twinkle twinkle little star
What time are you through up 'thar?
Smiling constant in the heaven,
I'm *only here till half-past seven.*

Twinkle twinkle Haley's comet,
Dashing to or rushing from it.
Up above the world you climb
While *I'm down here on overtime.*

Twinkle twinkle Man in the Moon,
Bet you wonder what I'm doon.
Up above the world you laugh,
I'm down here on time and a half.

Twinkle twinkle Milky Way,
You've never worked a ten-hour day.
Bet you wish that you were *me,*
I've earned four pounds fifty-three!

Remember what day it is

THIS IS THE LIFE...
HOW NICE IT
IS TO WAKE
UP IN THIS
SEMI-CONSCIOUS
STATE, REALISE
IT'S A SUNDAY MORNING AND
EXPERIENCE THAT WONDERFUL
RELIEF FLOODING ALL OVER ME...
I THINK I'LL LIE HERE ALL DAY.
I CAN JUST CLOSE MY EYES AND
LET MY SLEEP-
DRUGGED BRAIN
DRIFT OFF INTO—

HOLY MACKEREL!
—IT'S
MONDAY!!!

Better late than never

WOW! I'M CERTAINLY LATE THIS MORNING.... I'VE EVEN MISSED THE LATE - LATE CROWD...

I'M WITH THE "SO-LATE-IT'S-HARDLY-WORTH-GOING-IN-FOR" BRIGADE....

Punctuality above all things

THE VIEW FROM THIS WINDOW
IS POSITIVELY BREATHTAKING.
FAR AWAY TO MY RIGHT I CAN
SEE THE CHESTER PERRY
BUILDING LIKE A MATCH ON
                    THE
                    HORIZON..

STRAIGHT AHEAD I CAN SEE
THE NEW HOUSING ESTATE...

AND FAR AWAY TO MY LEFT WHAT
APPEARS TO BE A TOY TRAIN STEAMING
INTO A MINIATURE STATION . .

HOLY MACKEREL! IT'S THE
8.15 COMMUTER SPECIAL!

LATE AGAIN !!!

Try to relax

I'M TRYING A NEW EXPERIENCE TO EASE EVERYDAY TENSION... WORKING MY WAY RIGHT UP MY BODY... EASY DOES IT... EASY NOW... MY TOES ARE RELAXED... MY LEGS ARE RELAXED ...MY BODY IS RELAXED...MY ARMS ARE RELAXED... MY HANDS ARE RELAXED...MY FINGERS ARE RELAXED... EASY, DOES IT.. EASY... CALM BOY, **CALM**! MY NECK IS RELAXED, MY EYES ARE RELAXED NOW MY BRAIN... BLANKNESS.... UTTER BLANKNESS...THAT'S IT! I'M READY!!

PASS ME THOSE INVOICES...

Look after yourself

IS THAT YOU, JONES? BRISTOW HERE.
WOULD YOU MIND TELLING FUDGE
I WON'T BE IN THIS MORNING.
I CAUGHT MY THUMB IN THE TYPE-
WRITER YESTERDAY AND WHEN
I WOKE UP MY WHOLE BODY WAS A
MASS OF PAIN. I CAN HARDLY MOVE
A MUSCLE. I'M IN AGONY! ABSOLUTE
AGONY!! YOU'LL TELL HIM, WILL YOU
JONES?

INCIDENTALLY — THERE'S NO
POINT IN TRYING TO TRACE THIS
CALL... BY THE TIME YOU'VE
DONE IT I'LL HAVE RUN ROUND
THE CORNER AND DOWN THE
ROAD.....

Kick yourself occasionally

SCENE:	*The bookstall of a railway station.*
MAN:	Mr Bristow! It *is* Mr Bristow, isn't it? You remember me? Bernard Gentle – we used to work together at Effandee Holdings.
BRISTOW:	Of course I do. How is the old firm?
MAN:	Doing very nicely. It's not much fun, though, since you left to better yourself on that rainy morning eight years ago. I suppose you realise you'd have been Chief Buyer by now, if you'd stayed on?
BRISTOW:	Would you mind if I sat down? This bookstall is going round and round. . . .
MAN:	I always knew you'd make the top, Mr Bristow. Even then you had that certain something. I remember that rainy morning when you left to better yourself with the Chester-Perry Organisation. . . I turned to George Keig – you remember George?
BRISTOW:	Of course.
MAN:	George, I said, there goes a man with a tremendous future ahead of him. A man who refuses to allow himself to get into a rut – and I can see I was right. Cushy number you've landed, judging by the look of you.
BRISTOW:	(*Hesitant*) Well, er –
MAN:	Come on, Mr Bristow. . . . I'm no fool. It's only when you get to the top you can afford to dress *down* like that!

Put it in writing

A MERRY CHRISTMAS TO YOU ALL AND A PROSPEROUS AND HAPPY NEW YEAR TO EACH AND EVERY ONE OF YOU.

WELL, WELL, HOW NICE. THREE CHEERS FOR SIR REGINALD CHESTER-PERRY.

SIR REGINALD MY FOOT! LOOK AT THE SIGNATURE....

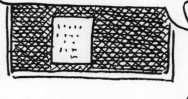

IT'S TOADY THOMPSON'S CHRISTMAS MESSAGE TO THE MANAGEMENT!!

Conform!

LOT OF CHESTER-PERRY PEOPLE IN THE PARK TODAY...

YOU CAN TELL A CHESTER-PERRY MAN A MILE OFF...

HE'S THE **BROWBEATEN** ONE WITH THE **SAD FACE**... THE **HANGDOG** EXPRESSION AND THE **NERVOUS TWITCH**...

TWITCH! TWITCH!

THE **CHESTER-PERRY TRADEMARK** !

Keep in trim

THE PERFECT BUSINESS
EXECUTIVE MUST POSSESS
ALL ROUND PHYSICAL
FITNESS...
**STRENGTH
AND STAMINA**
ARE IMPORTANT
TO OFFICE LIFE...

HERE WE GO THEN...
EXERCISE NUMBER ONE
TWO HOURS DEEP BREATHING
BY AN OPEN WINDOW.....

Moderation in all things

I'VE BEEN TRYING TO TEAR
IT IN HALF....

Keep your eyes on the next man

Keep your head above water

THERE IT IS... THE CHESTER-
PERRY BUILDING... PLOUGHING
IT'S WAY THROUGH THE STORMY
SEAS OF COMMERCE....

THAT'S MY OFFICE....

JUST BELOW THE **PLIMSOLL**
LINE......

Keep your eyes on the clock

THERE'S NOTHING TO IT.... A GRUNT FROM FUDGE MEANS IT'S **9.30** AM. THE RATTLE OF CUPS AND SAUCERS MEANS IT'S **10.15**... THE SIGHS OF RELIEF MEAN IT'S **11.30** AND THE SOUNDS OF STAMPEDING FEET MEANS FIVE MINUTES TO GO TO LUNCHTIME

CLOCKWATCHING BY EAR!!

Don't trust anyone

Get on with it!

Put on a front

Learn to control your feelings

BRISTOW: Well well, Toady Thompson, the firm's crawler. What's the occasion?

TOADY: I just bumped into Sir Reginald Chester-Perry, our beloved firm's founder, downstairs. Knocked him flying.

BRISTOW: What's he like?

TOADY: Try and imagine, if you can, two calm and serene blue eyes filled with compassion and understanding.

BRISTOW: Compassion and understanding?

TOADY: Compassion and understanding.

BRISTOW: Are we to take it that you consider yourself an expert on interpreting people's expressions?

TOADY: That's right.

BRISTOW: How would you describe this look?

(*He gazes at Toady steadily*)

TOADY: (*Staring back at him*) That's a mixture of pity... scorn...loathing and contempt.

BRISTOW: Hey – you're good!

Respect authority

Don't ask embarrassing questions

Don't be afraid
to accept praise

Get your regular eight hours

Don't be a clockwatcher

ANY MINUTE NOW AND IT'LL BE
TIME TO KNOCK OFF....

I CAN ALWAYS
TELL WHEN IT'S
NEARING TIME BY
LOOKING AT THE
FLOWERS IN THE
WINDOW BOXES
OF THE OFFICE
ACROSS THE STREET..

YES—THAT'S IT!
THE PETALS
ARE STARTING
TO FOLD UP!!

'NIGHT..

To do with tea

NEVER FILL A CUP TO THE BRIM...

REMEMBER —
ONE FULL CUP + EXTRA SUGAR = SOGGY
BISCUITS......

Take care of office equipment

MRS. PURDY—COME AND LOOK AT THIS... IT'S INCREDIBLE! THE TEA LEAVES IN THE BOTTOM OF MY CUP HAVE SETTLED THEMSELVES INTO EXACTLY THE SAME SHAPE AS THE DOODLES ON MY BLOTTER — LOOK!

SO STOP STIRRING YOUR TEA WITH YOUR PENCIL....

Remember, man is the measure of all things

Know your place

Be prepared to work hard

THERE IT IS — THE CHESTER-PERRY BUILDING....

A MIRACLE OF MODERN CONSTRUCTION.... TOOK AN ARMY OF WORKMEN TWO YEARS TO BUILD THAT PLACE...
JUST GIVE ME A PICKAXE, 24 HOURS AND A DEMOLITION ORDER!

Don't burn the candle at both ends

How to Win Friends and Influence People

Take five

*I had a little desk top
Nothing would it bear
But a single elbow
With some time to spare.
The head of our department
Flew into a flap
And all for the sake of
A little cat nap.*

Know your friends

I'M QUITE LOOKING FORWARD TO THE FIRM'S DINNER AND DANCE... IT'S A WONDERFUL OPPORTUNITY TO GET TOGETHER....

WHEN YOU COME TO THINK OF IT WE WORK SIDE BY SIDE FOR YEARS ON END AND WE HARDLY EVER GET TO KNOW EACH OTHER... EVEN IN THIS OFFICE WE ARE MORE OR LESS COMPLETE STRANGERS...

TOUCH WOOD!

Pay up or shut up

LET'S SEE NOW... RENT AND HOUSEKEEPING.. FARES...TWO WEEKS TEA MONEY... AND 50p I BORROWED FROM THE POSTBOY...

Look in the mirror every day

Be generous

Be tactful

LETTER TO MESSRS. GUN & FAMES
'DEAR SIR,
   OUR ORDER NUMBER DB 2392.
THE ABOVE ORDER WAS URGED BY
US ON 20TH ULTIMO BUT NO REPLY
HAS BEEN RECEIVED.

PERHAPS YOU WILL HAVE THE
COURTESY TO ANSWER.THIS TIME,
YOU **LAZY, SLOTHFUL, GOOD-FOR-NOTHING PIG!**

IF A REPLY HAS BEEN SENT
DURING THE LAST SEVEN DAYS
KINDLY DISREGARD THIS LETTER...

Be a sport

COMING TO THE CHESTER-PERRY SPORTS TOMORROW?

NOT ME. I'M NOT THE ATHLETIC TYPE. NEVER HAVE BEEN.

OH, BRISTOW. YOU COULD HAVE ENTERED **SOMETHING**... THE IMPORTANT THING ON THESE OCCASIONS IS NOT TO WIN BUT TO HAVE TAKEN PART.

Dress for the occasion

Keep your friendships in good repair

BRISTOW: Why, Miss Sunman – you're crying. Whatever's wrong? Someone been annoying you? Don't you feel well? Trouble at home? Row with the boy friend?

(*Rustle of paper*)

Poor thing! A whole page of typing and the carbon paper was in back to front! Never mind – you'll soon make it up. Tell you what to do.... Work through your lunch hour!

(*Sings*) If I can help somebody... Right! Now for a spot of tidying up. What have we here? A pile of invoices... a few requisitions... a wages slip... a date-stamp with my name scratched on the handle... a letter marked private and confidential and a box of pins....

JONES: Bristow – come away from my desk this minute....

BRISTOW: Are you using the dictating machine?

JONES: No. Do you want it?

BRISTOW: This won't take a second. (*Clears throat*) Testing... testing... 1-2-3-4-5-6-5-4-3-2-1 Mary had a little lamb... testing (*clears throat*) Dear Sir, Further to my letter of the fifth ultimo no reply has been received. Unless I hear from you forthwith I have no alternative other than to place the matter in the hands of my solicitors. Yours faithfully etc.

JONES: Strong stuff – who are you writing to?

BRISTOW: My pen pal – who else?

Getting the best out of a tea lady

TEA LADY: Tea up! Wet and warm and plenty of hard bake! Morning, Mr Jones.

JONES: Is it? Can't say I'd noticed. Daylight to me is just something on the other side of that window.

TEA LADY: Morning, Mr Bristow.

BRISTOW: Good morning, Mrs Purdy. What comestibles have you on board today?

TEA LADY: Get you! Comestibles, eh? Swallowed a dictionary, have you?

BRISTOW: Do you have any of your home-made, light-as-a-feather fairy cakes?

TEA LADY: I thought you didn't like my home-made, light-as-a-feather fairy cakes.

BRISTOW: What are you talking about? Finest paperweights in the business.

JONES: Your coconut macaroons look nice.

TEA LADY: *Are* nice.

BRISTOW: I think I'll take one of those. How much are they?

TEA LADY: Five pence each.

BRISTOW: (*Incredulous*) How much????

TEA LADY: Sorry, Mr Bristow. The price of coconut has gone up. Revolution in the country, or something.

BRISTOW: Isn't it *marvellous?* Every single, solitary action, man-made or otherwise, far or near, that happens on the face of this earth, hits me in the pocket.

JONES: Nice cup of hot tea for me. . . .

BRISTOW: You'll have it like the rest of us – served at room temperature! Mrs Purdy, I'll have a weakish Darjeeling with

	a sliver of lemon, a whisper of sugar, served in a white china cup, shaken not stirred.
TEA LADY:	Coming up!
	(*A gushing, splashing, hissing sound.*)
BRISTOW:	Holy mackerel!
JONES:	How long have you been here, Mrs Purdy?
TEA LADY:	Twelve years.
JONES:	Twelve years, man and boy, eh? And how many cups of tea have you made in that time?
TEA LADY:	Hundreds of thousands.
JONES:	What's the secret?
	(*An even louder gushing, splashing, hissing sound.*)
TEA LADY:	(*Shouting*) Trial and error.
BRISTOW:	I was wondering, Jones. How good are you at guessing ages?
JONES:	Not bad, why?
TEA LADY:	(*Giggles*) Give over.
BRISTOW:	Which do you think are the oldest – these rock-hard fairy cakes or these limp gingernuts.
	(*Door opens*)
FUDGE:	What the devil's going on out here. Get back to your desks you two! Good morning, Mrs Purdy.
TEA LADY:	Good morning, Mr Fudge.
FUDGE:	Those coconut things look nice. How much are they?
TEA LADY:	Five pence each.
FUDGE:	Is that all? I'll have a couple.
TEA LADY:	I'll be in in a minute.
	(*Door closes*)
	And to think I knew him when he hadn't two halfpennies to rub together. Mind you – that was a long time ago. A lot of water's flowed under the bridge since then.
BRISTOW:	I'll say. And judging by the taste of this rubbish, most of it

	via your teapot!
TEA LADY:	Very funny! (*Sudden change of mood*) Hello – what's this in your wastepaper basket? Why – it's yesterday's home-made, light-as-a-feather fairy cake. It must have fallen off your desk.
BRISTOW:	Fallen nothing – it was pushed!
TEA LADY:	Why you – !
	(*Tea trolley trundles off*)
JONES:	One of these days she's going to turn on you and give you a mouthful.
BRISTOW:	Let's hope so. It's bound to be an improvement on the mouthful I just had. No, Mrs Purdy is too easy going. Her heart's not in her job.
JONES:	No?
BRISTOW:	No. If you tell her the tea tastes awful she offers to take it back. Your *dedicated* tea lady must be prepared not only to *take* punishment, but to go on dishing it out!

Getting the best out of a temp

Stick with your own kind

AS A RULE I DON'T HAVE
ANYTHING TO DO WITH
ANIMALS BUT THIS BIRD
IS **DIFFERENT**....WE HAVE
SOMETHING IN COMMON

WE NEITHER OF US KNOW
WHERE THE NEXT MEAL
IS COMING FROM!

Don't gamble

BRISTOW: (*Picks up phone*)

Mary – put me through to Gun & Fames.

MARY: (*Giggles*) Saucy! Who do you want there?

BRISTOW: My opposite number, of course.

MARY: Putting you through. . . .

(*A few clicks over the telephone*)

VOICE: GUN & FAMES – tea boy speaking!

BRISTOW: I'd like to speak to someone about an order of ours.

VOICE: Troublemaker, eh? Hold on – I'll put you through.

(*A couple of clicks and then the distorted sound of a radio*)

VOICE: Hello?

BRISTOW: Hello. This is –

VOICE: Hold on. . . (*Shouts*) Turn that trannie down lads. . . (*Radio fades*). . . Hello! Anyone there?

BRISTOW: This is Bristow of –

VOICE: Hang on. . . (*Shouts*) Make a little less noise with those tea cups, boys. . . (*To Bristow*) You were saying?

BRISTOW: This is Bristow of Chester-Perry's?

VOICE: *Who* of Chester-Perry's?

BRISTOW: Bristow. B-R-I-S-T-O-W. B for Benjamin, R for Robert, I for Ivor, S for Stanley, T for Thomas, O for Oliver, W for Williams and my Christian names are –

(*A steady plick, plack, noise on the line*)

BRISTOW: Hello – can you hear me? Is there something wrong with this line?

VOICE: Just a moment. Steady on lads. (*To Bristow*) Sorry about that. Couple of the boys playing ping-pong with a cracked ball. Mr Bristow of Chester-Perry's, isn't it? What can I do for you?

BRISTOW:	It's about an order of ours we placed seven months ago.
VOICE:	No!
BRISTOW:	Yes!
VOICE:	As long ago as that? Don't think it is y'know.
BRISTOW:	It certainly *is*.
VOICE:	Hang on – (*Shouts*) George. . . what was the date on that paper aeroplane Fred was throwing about the other day? *Was* it now? I've got a chap here asking about it. What am I going to tell him?. . . right I'll try that. . . (*To Bristow*) Hello. . . you still there?
BRISTOW:	Still here.
VOICE:	The chap that's dealing with this is out of the office – would you like to call back at 11.30?
BRISTOW:	What's the time now?
VOICE:	10.30.
BRISTOW:	That's all right. I'll hang on.
VOICE:	I'd rather you didn't, if you don't mind. I've a few bets I want to get on. . . .
BRISTOW:	Do you intend to take any action on this or not?
VOICE:	Heads or tails?
BRISTOW:	Heads.
	(*Sound of coin dropping onto desk*)
VOICE:	Hard luck!

See yourself
as others see you

HITHER PAGE, COME STAND BY ME — IF THOU KNOWS'T ITS TELLING...
YONDER PEASANT WHO IS HE..?

Be mindful of others

JONES: You know, Bristow, we must be stupid, eating in the firm's canteen... we're just giving them back the money we work for... in fact, they make a fat profit out of us... an extravagant chef like Mr Gordon Blue doesn't work for peanuts, after all.

BRISTOW: The fact that he can experiment with food the way he does leaves a nasty taste in the mouth....

WAITRESS: Hello, Mr Bristow, hello Mr Jones. Long time no see.

JONES: Hello, my dear. The truth is we've been eating in the park of late, but now the weather's taken a turn for the worse we've decided to eat in the canteen.

BRISTOW: Return of the prodigal, as it were.

WAITRESS: Fatted calf's off!

JONES: What's on today?

WAITRESS: *Poulet en cocotte bonne femme.* Tender chunks of chicken cooked in mouth-watering wine sauce, garnished with egg.

BRISTOW: I'll try it – but don't bother about plates – put it straight into this doggy bag.

WAITRESS: Chips and peas?

BRISTOW: If you can squeeze them in.

WAITRESS: You'll have to wait a few minutes, dearie. Mr Gordon Blue is having a bite to eat.

JONES: Having a bite to eat when he should be preparing our lunch?

BRISTOW: Come on, Jones, be fair. You can't expect a Master Chef to work on an empty stomach.

JONES: Do you know, Bristow, I'm still a little boy at heart? I always eat the best bit first.

BRISTOW: So do I, as a rule – but when I'm in the firm's canteen I always save the best bit till last.

JONES: Surely that dried-up pie crust isn't the best bit?

BRISTOW: The best bit is any bit that covers up the name on the plate!

Lateral Thinking in the Office

Don't be afraid to adapt

I must go down to the Stores again
To the basement far below
And all I ask is a new pen
And the ink to make it go. . . .
And my knees knock and my toes curl and
My voice is breaking
And a grey mist on the storeman's face and
A great fist shaking.

Get down to basics

Use psychology

Be one jump ahead

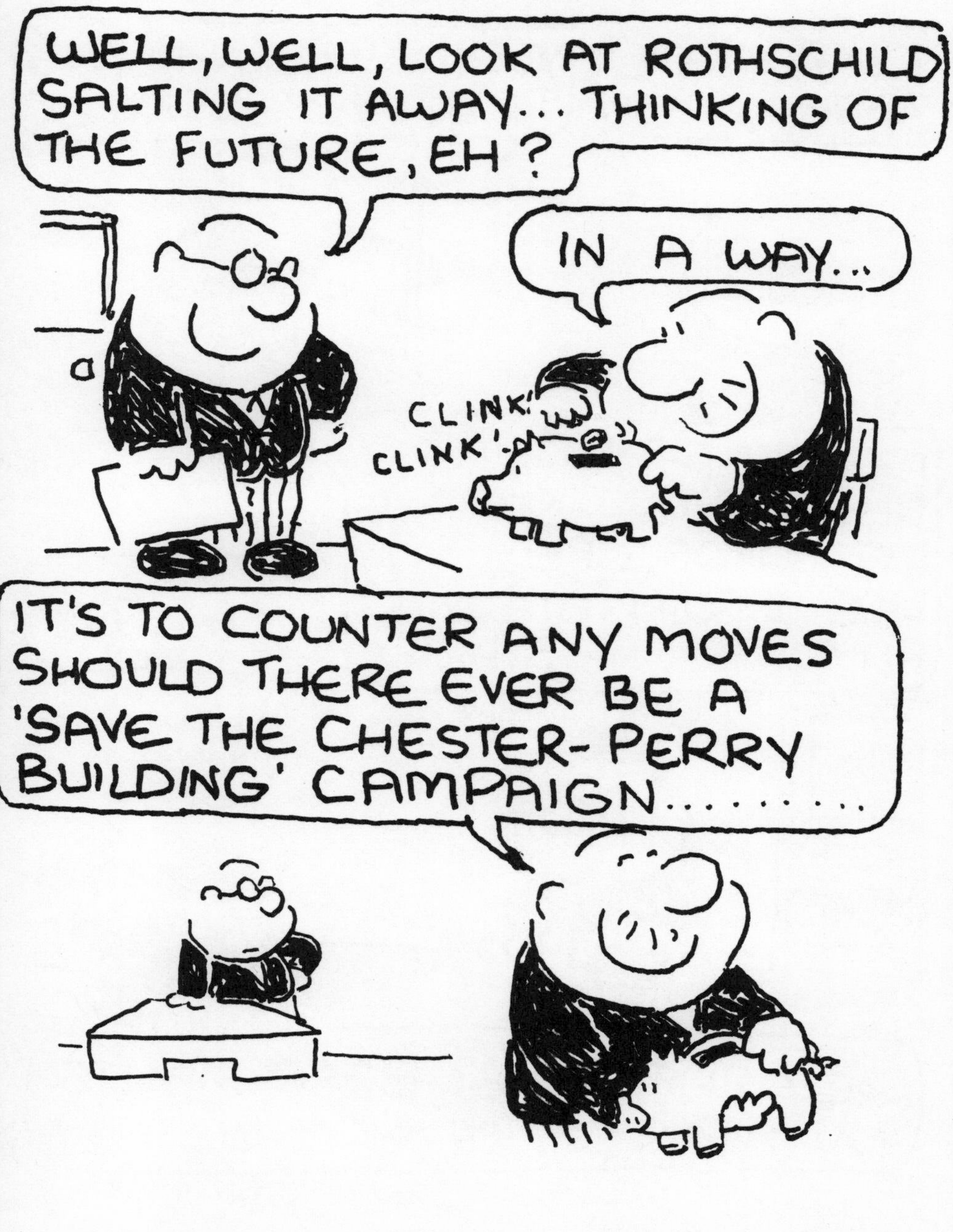

Remember, it's in the stars

Note how life imitates art

BRISTOW: Well, well, new cups and saucers at last. So elegant, too. I love the distinguished willow pattern.

TEA LADY: It tells a story too. Two employees are sneaking out early over a humpbacked bridge with Sir Reginald Chester-Perry in hot pursuit. . . .

BRISTOW: Quite charming. And I particularly like the way the little spoon is chained to the handle of the cup. . . The tall slim shape of the cup is most attractive, too. If one wishes to dunk one's biscuit one merely folds it in half. . .

(*Jones enters*)

JONES: Hallo, new crockery?

BRISTOW: What do you think?

JONES: (*Examines it*) Hopeless. Look how flat the saucer is. More like a plate if you ask me

BRISTOW: I quite agree, but considering the quality of the tea it does have one advantage. If one is drinking from the saucer the tea hits the back of the throat before the tastebuds know what's hit them.

Get your facts right

Read the signs

Be practical

Be calculating

THIS ADDING MACHINE IS WONDERFUL.... FOR ANYTHING THAT INVOLVES COUNTING ONE SIMPLY DEPRESS THE KEYS —

OUCH!

ONETWOTHREEFOURFIVESIXSEVENEIGHT....

Think ahead

JONES:	Have you heard the news?
BRISTOW:	News? News? – What news?
JONES:	Sir Reginald Chester-Perry, the firm's founder and multi-millionaire, is visiting the building.
BRISTOW:	Slumming, eh? Run out of petty cash, has he? Wish he'd get off my back....
	(*Door opens*)
BRISTOW:	Well, well, Miss Sunman of the typing pool.
SUNMAN:	Sir Reginald Chester-Perry is coming to the building. Isn't it exciting?
BRISTOW:	Why should it be exciting?
SUNMAN:	It may not be exciting to you but we girls have never seen him in the flesh. Have you?
JONES:	*I* have!
SUNMAN:	Honestly, Mr Jones? Do tell.
JONES:	I collided with him in the lift one day. Sent him flying, I did.
SUNMAN:	(*Gasp*) What happened? What did he say?
JONES:	Not a word. He just looked at me....
SUNMAN:	Go on... go on....
JONES:	Picture, if you can, two calm blue eyes filled with compassion and understanding....
BRISTOW:	Break it up, you two... he's here.
SUNMAN:	What do we do? What do we do?
BRISTOW:	We put a fire bucket on top of the door....
SUNMAN:	What a beautiful white Rolls-Royce (*Sighs*)... and look at that sumptuous black leather upholstery. When are you to get one of those, Mr Bristow?
BRISTOW:	Payday....

Think of your body as a piece of machinery

Remember, the looker-on sees more of the game

LOOK AT IT OUT THERE...
LOVELY SUNSHINE... AND I'M
STUCK IN A STUFFY OFFICE

WHAT WOULDN'T I GIVE TO
BE OUT THERE INSTEAD OF
ROTTING AWAY IN THIS DEAD
AND ALIVE HOLE ?

IT'S INHUMAN —THAT'S
WHAT IT IS — INHUMAN !

Be prepared to make changes

Use your head

Using a typewriter

IF, WHEN YOU GO TO TYPE 'THE QUICK BROWN FOX JUMPS OVER THE LAZY DOG'

AND IT COMES OUT 'UKT EOPB; MY+R? H+V LO·→F +NTY UKT ½DCI G+J'

YOUR TYPEWRITER NEEDS TO BE MOVED ONE INCH TO THE LEFT....

The Power of Positive Thinking

Be brave

In the Chester-Perry building,
Massive Chester-Perry building,
Was an office known as Buying,
Buying was their occupation
And their names were Jones & Bristow.

These two men they shared between them
All the phoning, all the filing,
All the dreary dreadful filing,
And their wages they were meagre,
Nine to five for just a pittance.

So they hated Chester-Perry,
Hated him with all their being,
And they lived for going home time,
Lovely glorious going home time,
Glad to leave the place behind them.

Sharp at five each his briefcase,
Then his bowler, then his brolly,
'Goodnight desk and goodnight office,
We will see you in the morning.
Quickly, Jones, we'll miss our buses'

Count your blessings

HASN'T THE DAY GONE QUICKLY?

ONLY ANOTHER FIVE MINUTES AND IT'LL BE '**FED UP TO THE BACK TEETH**' TIME...

Do not trust in miracles

Cut to interior firm's canteen. Mr Gordon Blue, master chef, is gazing out of the window.

GB: Curse this nine to five sunshine! Nobody eats in the canteen in this weather. Everyone takes sandwiches to the park.

     (Addresses Gladys) We have to lure them back. But how? We cannot improve upon the food or the decor. How then can we entice them back? There must be something we can do . . . some attraction we can offer.

     (He picks up and sips at a bottle of cooking sherry. Snaps fingers).

     I have it! Gladys, *(Looks at Gladys)* it all depends on you.

GLADYS: *(Firmly)* Topless waitresses are out.

GB: Proceed at once to the park.

GLADYS: *(Sexy)* You want me to lure them back?

GB: No. Paint all the benches.

     Phone rings. He picks up receiver

     Yes, this is Gordon Blue the master chef. What? Your delivery van has broken down. Sacre bleu! But I have a multitude of starving people to feed. *(Slams the phone down. Swigs sherry. Thinks. Snaps fingers).*

     Bring me five loaves and two fishes.

Enjoy your holidays

DEAR SLAVES
HAVING A REALLY **WILD**
TIME HERE AT FUNBOYS
SUR LA PLAGE....

THE FIRST DAY I WENT TO THE
MASKED BALL ... YESTERDAY
I WENT ON THE **MYSTERY
TOUR**...

SUMMING IT UP I DON'T KNOW
WHERE I'VE BEEN OR WHO
I'VE MET.....

Take advantage
of existing conditions

WHAT A PERFECT DAY...

A CLOUDLESS SKY OF AZURE
BLUE... BRILLIANT SUNSHINE...

...AND TO CROWN IT ALL, IF
I OPEN THE WINDOW THERE'S
JUST THE RIGHT AMOUNT OF
BREEZE...

Have the odd giggle

JONES: I say, Bristow – guess what? You remember that job in the Sits Vac column last week? I wrote up asking for an interview and it turned out the firm concerned was Myles & Rudge, the office across the street. What do you think?

BRISTOW: I think it's a good idea. To start with you won't have so far to come in the mornings.

JONES: Then my mind is made up. Let's face it, I'm not getting any younger and the prospects of my becoming Chief Buyer are practically non-existent. Not only that but I'm bored with the whole set-up – I'm sick to my stomach of the people that work here – the wages are appalling – the conditions intolerable –

BRISTOW: Steady, Jones. Leave one loophole in case you don't land the job!

JONES: Do you think if I ask for half as much again as I get here they'll wear it?

BRISTOW: Don't see why not. After all, that's what you're going after the job for – to *better* yourself, isn't it? No point in changing for the same *money*. No, you ask for half as much again.

          So they laugh you out of the building. . . .

Look on the bright side

THERE'S A LOVELY RAINBOW OUT THERE...

SUPPOSED TO BE A CROCK OF GOLD WHERE THE RAINBOW ENDS.....

OUT OF SHEER CURIOSITY LET ME JUST—

GOOD HEAVENS—
IT'S **TRUE**!

IT FINISHES UP OUTSIDE THE
ACCOUNTS!

Wax lyrical every now and then

THIS IS THE LIFE..........

A PERFECT SPOT...A BEAUTIFUL EVENING... EVERYTHING PAINTED IN ORANGE AND GOLD... A BIRD CHEEPS HERE... A BIRD CHIRPS THERE... IN YONDER FIELD A WEARY PLOUGHMAN HOMEWARD PLODS...........

AND FAR AWAY ON THE HORIZON THE PURPLE CHESTER-PERRY BUILDING...

Savour every moment

JONES: What surprises me is why a Master Chef like Mr Gordon Blue works in a dump like this.

BRISTOW: Ah but Mr Gordon Blue isn't like other chefs. He has a wife and five starving children to support....

FRUITY VOICE: Morning, you two

BRISTOW: Well, well, Mr Crewe, the firm's gourmet. What are you doing in this neck of the woods?

CREWE: I dropped in to sample today's speciality. I've been coming here a lot recently, ever since Mr Gordon Blue started his international season.

BRISTOW: International season?

CREWE: Yes. He spent his Christmas holidays touring the continent for rare and exotic dishes with which to titillate our jaded palates.

BRISTOW: I see. Let me guess. Toad in the hole *espanol*, Shepherds pie *parisienne*, Liver and bacon *italiano*, sausage, double egg and chips *à la grecque?*

CREWE: No – he did it properly. Last Monday, f'r instance I had Hungarian goulash... Tuesday I partook of his Spanish omelette... Wednesday I ploughed through his German pot roast with potato dumplings... Thursday I went Greek... Friday, Italian, today it's French I believe and tomorrow Russian.

BRISTOW: Will you be here?

CREWE: No, I shall be on holiday.

BRISTOW: Going away?

CREWE: No. I *was* going abroad but I've had to cancel it... Continental tummy!

Enjoy God's scenery

IN A KIND OF OFF-BEAT WAY I'VE GROWN QUITE ATTACHED TO THAT PLANT IN THE WINDOW BOX ACROSS THE STREET...

BY LEANING WELL BACK IN MY CHAIR, COVERING MY LEFT EYE AND SQUINTING THROUGH MY RIGHT FINGERS I CAN ELIMINATE ALL THE SURROUNDING BRICKWORK... ALL I CAN SEE IS A BUNCH OF COOL GREEN LEAVES....

SUDDENLY I'M MILES AWAY IN THE HEART OF THE COUNTRYSIDE

Recognise a sense of humour

BRISTOW: Our grapevine is a marvellous thing. You've only got to say something and before you know where you are it's all over the building. Especially malicious gossip . . . That spreads in . . . Jones – how long does it take you to walk round the building?

(Door opens)

TEA LADY: *(Shouts)* Tea up! Wet and warm and plenty of hard bake!

BRISTOW: Mrs Purdy – keep your voice down. Sir Reginald Chester-Perry, our beloved firm's founder, multi-millionaire and business tycoon is in the building.

TEA LADY: *(Despairingly) Another* cup to wash up!

BRISTOW: Just a minute – where are you going?

TEA LADY: Back to the kitchen. Better let them know the champagne and caviar set are here. . . .

BRISTOW: But what about us?

TEA LADY: Beer and skittle brigade!

(Door slams)

BRISTOW: Would you believe it! The sheer nerve! Making us wait while she goes and has a chat. . . .

(Door opens)

SUNMAN: Mr Bristow – Mr Bristow!

BRISTOW: Calm yourself, Miss Sunman and speak slowly and distinctly. What is it *this* time?

SUNMAN: Mr Bristow – I've just seen Sir Reginald Chester-Perry in the flesh. My word, he has aged! His face is lined with worry!

BRISTOW: Worry? Do you think a multi-millionaire about to embark on a three-month holiday in the Bahamas is worried? Worry, my foot – those are laughter-lines!!!

Crack the odd joke

POOR OLD JONES...
HAS FUDGE GOT IT
IN FOR **HIM**...

FUDGE CORNERED HIM OVER BY THE
WINDOW AND STARTED RANTING AND
RAVING LIKE A MANIAC...

JONES BROKE CLEAR BUT FUDGE
CAUGHT HIM BY THE FILING CABINET
AND STARTED
ON HIM AGAIN...

SINCE THEN THEY'VE BEEN ALL
ROUND THE ROOM.....

WALL TO WALL CARPETING!

Be philosophical

ALL THINGS CONSIDERED THIS
ISN'T A BAD JOB... IT HAS
IT'S UPS AND DOWNS, OF
COURSE, BUT WHAT JOB HASN'T?

AND LET'S GIVE CREDIT WHERE
IT'S DUE, THE MANAGEMENT
ARE PRETTY FREE AND EASY...

WE CAN COME IN ANYTIME
BEFORE NINE AND LEAVE
ANYTIME AFTER FIVE......

Learn something new every day

BRISTOW: If I could draw a circle around a moment in time and say this is the most boring moment of my life, I would draw that circle now... and another *now*... and another *now*... and *now*... and now....

JONES: Bristow – how are you getting on with that order on Messrs Gun & Fames?

BRISTOW: Don't speak to me about Gun & Fames! I've never known such a bunch of time-wasting layabouts.

JONES: Keep pressing them.

BRISTOW: No. They annoyed me so much yesterday I need a sixty-day cooling-off period.

JONES: Let's go to lunch in the park.

BRISTOW: No, let's give the canteen a bit of support.

JONES: A firm's canteen marches on its stomachs, remember. You're just a crawler, that's all....

BRISTOW: Crawler? That's rich – coming from you.... Why are you carrying a copy of the House Journal around in your pocket? Going to read it during your lunch hour?

JONES: Don't be stupid – with the amount of rain that fell during the night the bench may be damp!

Look after yourself

Publish and be damned!

SUNMAN: Mr Bristow!

BRISTOW: Well, well, Miss Sunman of the typing pool. What can I do for you?

SUNMAN: I wonder whether you'd mind listening to some of your dictation. I can't make head nor tail of it.

BRISTOW: Fire away.

SUNMAN: (*Clears throat*) Re. your letter of the 14th. 'What a lot of nonsense! What rubbish! What a waste of time, money and materials. What a shambles! What rot! What bunkum! What piffle! What drivel!' What does it *mean*, Mr Bristow?

BRISTOW: It means I left the machine on when I was skimming through the Bumper Spring Number of the House Journal.

SUNMAN: You mean you didn't like it?

BRISTOW: I thought it a sugary, syrupy, saccharine-sweet, honeyed piece of humbug. I know that sounds like sour grapes but I mean every word.

SUNMAN: But do you realise it's the Golden Anniversary number? 50 years. That's 200 issues. I think it's a remarkable achievement.

BRISTOW: Remarkable? Considering each issue is worse than the one before it, I'd say it's a downright miracle!

SUNMAN: Just because *your* name wasn't in it.

BRISTOW: That's the only way they get anyone to read it, by filling it with names. After all it's a human weakness to want to see your name in print. Personally, I think anyone who's never been mentioned ought to go down on the firm's Roll of Honour.

SUNMAN: Ooh, you are awful!

(*Door slams*)

JONES: How is it, Bristow, that Tillie's Employment Bureau always send us the most attractive, half-witted girls?

BRISTOW: Standing order.

Remember, every cloud has a silver lining

I HATE THE WINTER... IT'S DARK WHEN WE ARRIVE AND DARK WHEN WE LEAVE....

MIND YOU — IT DOES HAVE IT'S COMPENSATIONS.... BEFORE I START WORK I CAN SIT BACK, GAZE OUT OF THE WINDOW AND WATCH THE DAWN BREAKING!

Weigh up the pros and cons

BRISTOW: What a lovely morning. Bright sunshine and blue skies. Good to be alive on a day like this. Kind of weather that makes you want to bounce around in sheer well being . . . I know, I'll take the day off sick! (*Sings*) 'Oh what a beautiful morning . . .' So they'll be short handed. Who cares? What's one buying clerk more or less in a place the size of Chester-Perry's? After all, I'm not the only one in the Buying Department. There's always Jones. And if he can't cope old Fudge will have to lend a hand. Time he did some work anyway, instead of stamping round yelling and screaming at the top of his voice. One of these days I'll tell him so. 'Look, Mr Fudge,' I'll say, 'I've been with the Chester-Perry Organisation for eight long years and during that time you've been rude to me sixteen thousand times. I've reached the end of my tether. Find yourself another whipping boy,' I shall say, 'because I'm out. O.U.T. Get that? O for Overjoyed, U for Unemployed and T for Temporarily (I hope!).' That's what I'll do then. I'll ring in, make my excuse and spend the day in the park (*Sings*) 'There's a bright, golden haze in the meadow. . .' Hello! – do I spy a couple of clouds? Mmh! Not so nice as I thought. I don't think I'll take the day off after all. When you take a day off you want *gorgeous* weather. No point in wasting a good excuse like sickness for weather that's only so-so.

I'll save it for a rainy day.

Office Proverbs

Bless this house

This is the house that Reg built,
This is the tea they serve in the house that Reg built,
This is the clerk that drinks the tea they serve in
the house that Reg built,
This is the man that bosses the clerk that drinks the
tea they serve in the house that Reg built.

GET ON WITH YOUR WORK!

That is the shout that frightens the clerk who does
what he's told
To hold down his job in the house that Reg built.

Judge not
that ye be judged

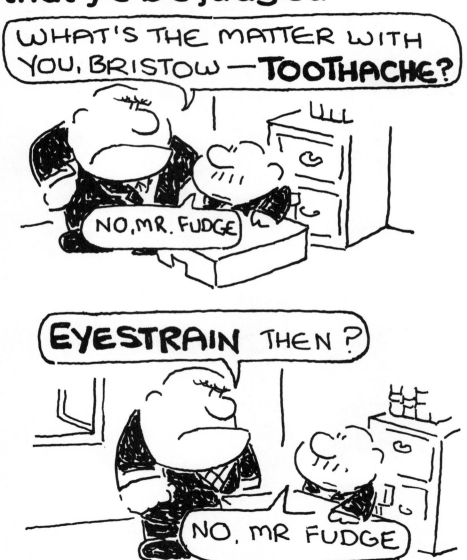

TOOTHACHE AND EYESTRAIN
INDEED!
THE MAN'S
A FOOL...

I'VE BEEN GIVING HIM THE
SAME LOOK FOR NEARLY
EIGHT YEARS AND HE **STILL**
DOESN'T RECOGNISE
DUMB INSOLENCE!!

The grass is always greener..

LOOK AT THAT!

BLUE SKIES...BRILLIANT
SUNSHINE... FLOWERS
BURSTING FROM THEIR
WINDOW BOXES...
FAREWELL COLD WINTER!

OH, TO BE A SALES REP.
NOW THAT SPRING IS
HERE.....

Let sleeping dogs lie

BRISTOW: There it is – the Chester-Perry building... I can't understand Sir Reginald. I know he has the name written right across the front of the building but it's too low down. He ought to have it written along the top of the building – where it can be seen from miles away. The R.L. Chester-Perry Company Ltd. (P.S. If you can read this you're too close!)

BRISTOW: Morning, Jones.

JONES: (*Cross*) Where's my date-stamp?

BRISTOW: Date-stamp?

JONES: Yes, the last time you had it, you put it in the top right-hand drawer of your desk.

(Bristow rummages through improbably-packed drawers.)

BRISTOW: By Jingo! You're right! When did I borrow that?

JONES: *(Breathes on date-stamp and laconically stamps pad on Bristow's desk. Stalks off back to his own desk.)*

BRISTOW: (*Reads pad*) 8th August '71. (*He shrugs. His attention is drawn to a file marked 'Urgent', sticking out of a drawer. He picks it up and blows a cloud of dust from its cover. He looks surprised.*) Amazing the way these offices harbour the dust. It's only been on my desk a fortnight.

Never a borrower or a lender be

SUGAR, MILK, TEA, BISCUITS AND OFF WE GO... HOLD ON! IT'S THURSDAY....

PLEASE DO NOT ASK FOR CREDIT AS A REFUSAL OFTEN OFFENDS

All work and no play...

JONES: Well, Bristow. What shall we start on – filing, dictation, correspondence or invoicing?

BRISTOW: Whatever turns you on.

JONES: How about a game of desk-top football?

BRISTOW: Bags Arsenal.

JONES: I'll be Chelsea. Got any coins?

           (*Coins rattling on desk top*)

BRISTOW: Arsenal to kick off.

JONES: Why should Arsenal get the kick-off?

BRISTOW: My coins.

JONES: (*Sighs*) Go on, then – hold it! Here comes Fudge!

           (*Door opens*)

FUDGE: Bristow – get on to Messrs Gun & Fames and chase up this order. It was placed seven months ago.

           (*Door slams*)

JONES: Holy smoke! That was close. I could have sworn he saw the coins on your desk, yet he didn't say a word.

BRISTOW: Saw them? Of course he saw them. Too embarrassed to say anything. Probably thought I was counting my wages. . . .

JONES: I should get on with it if I were you. . . .

BRISTOW: I'm going to. I'm just waiting for the dust to settle.

If at first you don't succeed..

GANGWAY!
GANGWAY

I'VE JUST BEEN
UP TO SICK
BAY TO HAVE
MY THUMB
TREATED....

I MUST GET
BACK ON THE
ADDING MACHINE
BEFORE I LOSE
MY NERVE....

Don't bite the hand that feeds you

JONES: News! news! Messrs Gun & Fames are trying to POACH our Master Chef Mr Gordon Blue. Rumour has it they've offered more DOUGH.

BRISTOW: RAISIN salary eh? No use getting STEAMED up about a mere TRIFLE. He won't DESSERT us, not AFTERS all we've done for him. I'll PUD it to him straight and if he argues I'll DUFF him up.

JONES: (*To himself*) JELLY good.

BRISTOW: (*Picks up phone*) Canteen? I'd like to speak to Mr Gordon Blue. My name is Bristow. BRISTOW. B-R-I-S-T-O-W. B for baked beans, R for roast potatoes, I for Irish stew, S for sausage, T for toad, O for 'ole as in toad in the 'ole and W for Wiener Schnitzel. What's that? he's busy. . . the delivery van has broken down. Don't worry about that. . . give him five loaves and a couple of fish. . . don't speak to me like that. . . damn SAUCE. . . and the same to you with knobs of butter on! Ah – is that Mr Gordon Blue?

GORDON BLUE: What do you want?

BRISTOW: I understand Myles & Rudge have approached you with a proposition.

GORDON BLUE: You have no right to GRILL me in this MANNA. I MUSTARDmit I've BEAN approached but I'm thinking it over.

BRISTOW: You don't think we'd BATTER MEAT and SALT it out? After all, your reputation is at STEAK.

GORDON BLUE: LETTUCE leave it as it is.

BRISTOW: You mean LIVER and let LIVER?

GORDON BLUE: FARE enough. Ciao.

BRISTOW: CHOW!

Actions speak louder than words

A rose by any other name...

RIGHT, LADIES... HERE IS TODAY'S MENU... SOUP, BOILED FISH, MEAT PIE, TINNED PEARS...

MR. GORDON BLUE — THE DIRECTORS WILL BE DINING ON THE PREMISES. WHAT WILL THEY BE EATING?

EXACTLY THE SAME AS EVERYONE ELSE, OF COURSE.....

CONSOMME CELESTINE... SOLE VERONIQUE... GIGOT D'AGNEU EN PÂTE... POIRES BELLE HÉLÈNE.....

Remember, a fool and his money...

MISS SUNMAN:	Here's that letter you wanted
BRISTOW:	Miss Sunman, I think it's high time you treated yourself to a change of carbon papers. Just look at these copies.
SUNMAN:	What's the matter with them?
BRISTOW:	What's the matter with them? You can't read them, that's what's the matter with them.
SUNMAN:	You can read the first three. How many copies do you want?
BRISTOW:	Six.
SUNMAN:	Six. You want six, did you say? (*Snorts*)
	(*Door slams*)
JONES:	You were lucky there. I thought she'd come in to clobber you for a few bob for Mary Grant's wedding present.
BRISTOW:	No chance.
	(*Door opens*)
SUNMAN:	Ah, Mr Bristow....
BRISTOW:	Back so soon, Miss Sunman?
SUNMAN:	Yes, I'm collecting for Mary Grant's wedding present
BRISTOW:	Sorry, you should have called on Friday.
SUNMAN:	I did. I couldn't find you.
BRISTOW:	You couldn't find me hanging from the window-ledge? Anyway, I've never heard of this Mary whatever-her-name-is. Why should I contribute to someone I don't know?
SUNMAN:	Of course you do. She's the little blonde who shrieked with laughter when you banged your head on the door of the typing pool.
BRISTOW:	Mmh! I remember – and suggest you try elsewhere. Tell her I'm still suffering from loss of memory!

Cleanliness is next to godliness

STATE OF THIS PLACE! IT HASN'T BEEN TOUCHED FOR DAYS... DUST ON THE DESKS... DUST ON THE LAMPSHADES... DUST ON THE CABINETS... DUST EVERYWHERE!

BEATS ME WHAT THE CLEANING LADY DOES WITH HER TIME....

WHO'S BEEN SITTING IN **MY** CHAIR?

Forewarned is forearmed

TEA LADY: Haven't you finished with your cup yet? Your tea break is from 10.15 till 10.30.

BRISTOW: That may be your definition of our tea break. *My* tea break starts ten minutes before the rising of your trolley and ends ten minutes after the going-down of the same.

JONES: I say, Mrs Purdy. . . come and look at this. The tea leaves at the bottom of my cup have settled themselves into exactly the same shape as the doodles on my blotter. Look!

TEA LADY: So stop stirring your tea with your pencil. (*Guffaws*)

BRISTOW: Do you know – I haven't seen her that amused since the day I spilt scalding hot coffee down my shirt-front.

JONES: Well, Mrs Purdy. What do you make of it? Tell me about tall buildings and long journeys and beautiful strangers.

TEA LADY: First cross my palm with last week's tea money. You had a rough time of it, judging by your bill.

JONES: I'll say. Fudge had me in his office every day.

TEA LADY: So I see. Monday, tea and cakes; Tuesday, tea and a sedative; Wednesday, tea and a sedative; Thursday, tea and cakes; Friday, tea and a sedative.
Now let's have a look. Tut, tut. . . I see a disappointment.

JONES: Disappointment?

TEA LADY: When the tannin cluster is in the ascendancy a disappointment is imminent. (*Declaims*) The moving finger writes and having written, moves on, nor all the piety nor wit shall lure them back to cancel half a line, nor all thy tears wash out a word of theirs.

(*Door closes*)

JONES: Well! She makes a good cup of tea, anyway.

BRISTOW: (*Shocked*) Jones! I knew the Chester-Perry Organisation had got hold of you, but I never realised the full extent of the take-over. Even your taste-buds have been brainwashed!

Patience is a virtue

EIGHT HOURS TO GO... **EIGHT** HOURS! JUST THINK OF IT. EIGHT MORE HOURS...THAT'S FOUR HUNDRED AND EIGHTY MINUTES. FOUR HUNDRED AND EIGHTY TIMES SIXTY IS.... TWENTY EIGHT THOUSAND EIGHT HUNDRED !!!
THERE ARE TWENTY EIGHT THOUSAND EIGHT HUNDRED **SECONDS** TO GO !!!

ONE...TWO...
THREE..FOUR...

Turn the other cheek

Practice makes perfect

Silence is golden

The road to hell is paved with good intentions

I'VE BEEN THINKING... THERE'S ABSOLUTELY NOTHING TO STOP ME WALKING OUT THROUGH THAT DOOR AND JUST NEVER COMING BACK...

SO WHY DON'T I DO IT? I'VE NO COMMITMENTS...NO **TIES**...ALL I'VE GOT TO DO IS TO SUMMON UP THE COURAGE TO MAKE THE FINAL BREAK.... BY GEORGE I'LL DO IT! I'LL DAMN WELL DO IT!

All's well
that ends well